Ages 6-7
Key Stage 1

Supports the National Curriculum Key Stage 1

Spelling

PaRRagon

Bath • New York • Singapore • Hong Kong • Cologne • Delhi
Melbourne • Amsterdam • Johannesburg • Auckland • Shenzhen

Written by Betty Root and Nina Filipek
Educational Consultant: Martin Malcolm
Illustrated by Simon Abbot

This edition published by Parragon in 2012

Parragon
Queen Street House
4 Queen Street
BATH, BA1 1HE, UK
www.parragon.com

ISBN 978-1-4454-7760-2

Printed in China

Helping your child

Children learn to spell by looking and writing. If your child finds a word difficult, try to follow this pattern:

LOOK at the word; COVER UP the word; WRITE the word; CHECK the word.

Encourage your child to say each letter as it is written.

Try to find a quiet place to work.

Stop before your child grows tired and finish the page another time.

Work through the pages in the right order – they get more difficult as you go on.

Always give your child lots of encouragement and praise.

The answers to the activities begin on page 122.

Contents

Contents

Writing names

Write the name of each child next to the correct number.
Remember that names begin with a capital letter.

1.

2.

3.

4.

5.

Lily

6.

Josh

1. _____

2. _____

3. _____

4. _____

5. _____

6. _____

First letter sounds

Choose one letter to make
each word.

a	b	c	d	e	f	g	h

e_gg   A_nt

c_ap   d_og

g_oat   h_en

_b_ o x   _fh_ ish

Copy the words in order from
a to h.

1. a _a a a a a all_

2. b _b ox_

3. c _cap_

4. _goat_

5. _han_

6. _dog_

7. _fhish_

8. _egg_

Look at the picture.
Can you spot something that
begins with each letter?

| i | j | k | l | m | n | o | p | q | r |

Fill in the gaps.

The __ing and __ueen had lots
of pets.

They had a __ion, and a __onkey
and a __ig.

They had an __wl in a __est.

They had a __abbit with big ears.

They fed them all on __elly and
__ce-cream.

Put the words you made in order, from i to r.

1. i _____

2. j _____

3. k _____

4. l _____

5. m _____

6. n _____

7. o _____

8. p _____

9. q _____

10. r _____

Choose one letter to make
each word.

| s | t | u | v | w | x | y | z |

t ap

v an

w asp

y ellow

z ip

u mbrella

_x_-ray   _s_un

Copy the words in order from s to z.

1. s un

2. top

3. umbrella

4. _____

5. _____

6. _____

7. _____

8. _____

Write a word under each picture. Copy out the words in alphabetical order. Use a dictionary to help you.

_ _ _ _ _

_ _ _ _ _ _

_ _ _

_ _ _ _ _ _ _ _

_ _ _ _

a p e

___ ___ ___   ___ ___ ___ ___ ___ ___ ___ ___

Alphabetical order:

1. ape

2.

3.

4.

5.

6.

7.

8.

Food alphabet

Write a word under each
picture. Copy out the words
in alphabetical order. Use a
dictionary to help you.

ice-cream

_ _ _ _

_ _ _

_ _ _ _ _

_ _ _ _ _

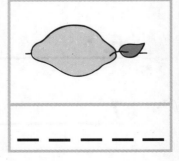

_ _ _ _ _

Alphabetical order:

1. ice-cream

2. _____

3. _____

4. _____

5. _____

6. _____

w words

These <u>w</u> words ask questions:

when	what	where
why	who	was

Write them in the questions below. Remember to write a capital letter if the word is at the beginning of a sentence.

1. _____ time is it?

2. _____ are you going?

3. _____ is your best friend?

4. _____ is your birthday?

5. _____ are you sad?

6. _____ it a good game?

Short vowel 'a'

Write the letter <u>a</u> to finish
each word.

b _ _ t   h _ _ t

c_ _ t   r _ _ t

Copy each word under the
right picture.

_____   _____

_____   _____

Fill in the missing words.
Choose from the box.

dad	fat	bag	map

1. I put my books
in a _____ .

2. My _____
reads to me.

3. I look at a _____
to find the way.

4. My dog is _____ .
She eats too much.

Write the letter <u>e</u> to finish
each word.

b __ d   n __ t

r __ d   w __ b

Copy each word under the
right picture.

_____   _____

_____   _____

Fill in the missing words.
Choose from the box.

| ten | fed | pen | wet |

1. I have

_____ toes.

2. I _____

the rabbits.

3. I write with

a _____ .

4. My dog fell in the pond.

He was _____ .

Write the letter <u>i</u> to finish
each word.

p_g   s__x

w__g   p_n

Copy each word under the
right picture.

_____   _____

_____   _____

Fill in the missing words.
Choose from the box.

| dig | did | big | lick |

1. At the seaside I
_____ in the sand.

2. The cat likes to
_____ its paws.

3. An elephant is a
very _____ animal.

4. Sam _____ not
go to bed early.

Write the letter <u>o</u> to finish
each word.

d_g   f_x

m_p   l_g

Copy each word under the
right picture.

_____   _____

_____   _____

Fill in the missing words.
Choose from the box.

| got | hot | on | top |

1. I _____ a new
bike for my birthday.

2. The bird sat
_____ the fence.

3. The boy ran to the
_____ of the hill.

4. When the sun shines
it is _____ .

Short vowel `u`

Write the letter <u>u</u> to finish
each word.

b__s   c__p

d__ck   s__n

Copy each word under the
right picture.

_____   _____

_____   _____

Fill in the missing words.
Choose from the box.

| mum | mud | run | hug |

1. We had to

_____ to catch the bus.

2. I _____ my

teddy at bedtime.

3. My _____ takes

me to school.

4. At the farm I got _____

on my shoes.

Second chance

Write the missing letter to finish each word. Read the words.

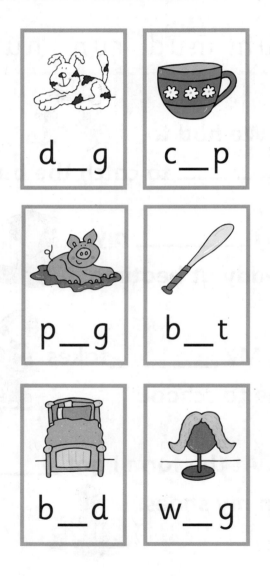

d__g

c__p

p__g

b__t

b__d

w__g

c _ _ t

f _ _ x

w _ _ b

d _ _ ck

n _ _ t

s _ _ n

r _ _ t

b _ _ s

All these words are muddled up. Write them correctly. You can use a dictionary to help you.

	wrong ✗	right ✓
	d e b	_____
	i b b	_____
	g g e	_____
	t c a	_____

	wrong ✘	right ✓
	o y b	_____
	a c r	_____
	e b e	_____
	u b s	_____
	t a b	_____

ch sound

Write <u>ch</u> to make each word. LOOK at the word. COVER it up. WRITE it on the line below. CHECK if you are right!

_ _ air

_ _ ick

_ _ erry

 _ _ ildren

 _ _ ocolate

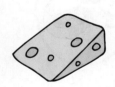 _ _ eese

 _ _ ur _ _

Look carefully

Say the name of each picture and choose <u>ch</u> or <u>ck</u> to finish it. Write the words that end in <u>ch</u> inside the hutch, and the words that end in <u>ck</u> inside the sack.

wat __ __

bri __ __

swit __ __

du __ __

so __ __

wit __ __

hu<u>ch</u>

_____

_____

_____

sa<u>ck</u>

_____

_____

_____

Wordsearch for sh

Look in the blue box for words that begin or end with <u>sh.</u>
Copy each word next to the right picture.

s	h	a	r	k	n	b
h	m	f	o	d	e	r
e	d	i	s	h	s	u
e	h	s	r	u	l	s
p	s	h	e	d	o	h

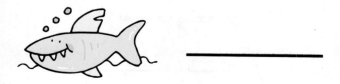 _____

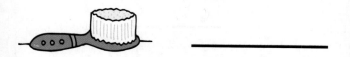 _____

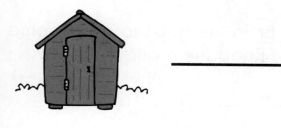 _____

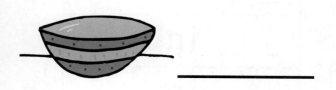 _____

 _____

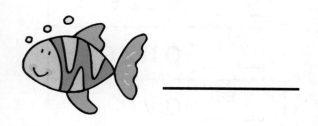 _____

br sound

Write <u>br</u> in the gaps to make some words. Read them out.

_ _	ain
_ _	anch
_ _	oom
_ _	idle
_ _	ook
_ _	ing
_ _	im
_ _	eeze
_ _	onze
_ _	ave

Draw a line to match each word to a picture.

bridge

brown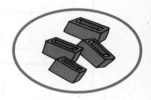

bread

brother

bricks

Write <u>cr</u> in the gaps to make some words. Read them out.

_ _y
_ _ash
_ _ew
_ _isp
_ _umb
_ _unch
_ _eak
_ _eam
_ _ate
_ _ocodile

Look at the picture clues.
Write the letters cr in the
correct place in the crossword.

Across   **Down**

dr or tr?

Write <u>dr</u> or <u>tr</u> in the gaps to make some words.

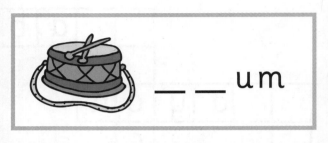 _ _ um

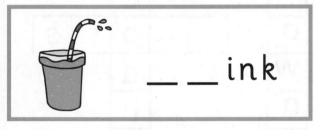 _ _ ink

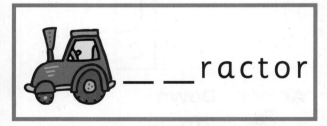 _ _ ractor

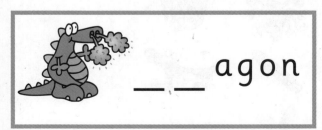 _ _ agon

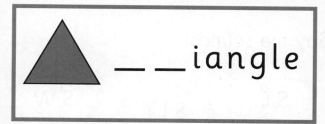 _ _iangle

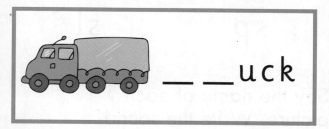 _ _uck

Cover up the words you wrote.
Write a <u>dr</u> or <u>tr</u> word in each gap.

1. It's green and

   blows out fire. _____

2. You bang on it.

                 _____

3. You have it when

   you are thirsty. _____

4. A farmer drives it.

                 _____

Say the sounds:

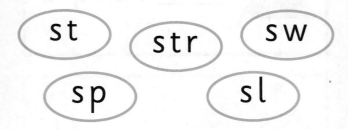

st   str   sw

sp   sl

Say the name of each picture. Write the sound to match the picture.

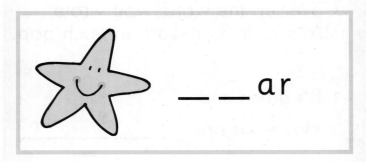

_ _ ar

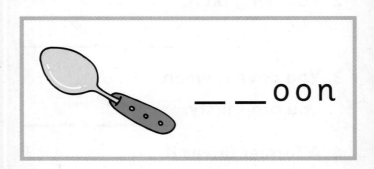

_ _ oon

 _ _ amp

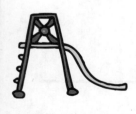 _ _ ing

 _ _ _ awberry

 _ _ ide

Look in the blue box for words that begin with <u>bl</u>, <u>cl</u> or <u>fl</u>. Copy each word next to the right picture.

c	l	c	b	l	u	e
l	f	l	b	l	f	e
f	l	o	w	e	r	s
l	a	c	l	o	u	d
g	g	k	c	h	l	b
z	b	k	b	b	l	l
y	l	b	l	a	c	k

 _____

th sound

Write <u>th</u> to make each word.
LOOK at the word. COVER it
up. WRITE it on the line below.
CHECK if you are right!

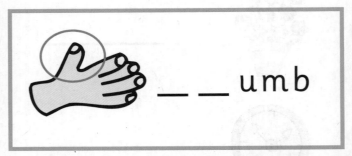 _ _ umb

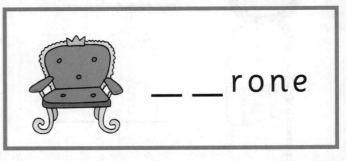 _ _ rone

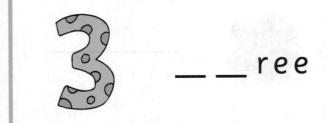 _ _ ree

 _ _istle

 ba _ _

 too_ _brush

3+2 = 5
9-6 = 3 ma _ _ s

Say the name of each
picture. Spell the word
next to each picture.

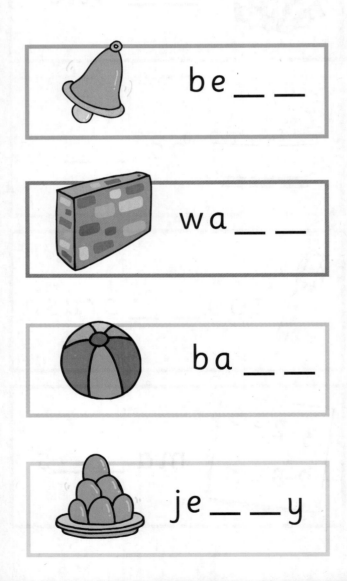

b e __ __

w a __ __

b a __ __

j e __ __ y

umbre _ _ a

ro _ _ er skate

ye _ _ ow

ba _ _ oons

caterpi _ _ ars

Double letters: dd, rr, tt, ss, zz

Say the name of each picture. Spell the word next to each picture.

bo __ __ le

ke __ __ le

te __ __ y

che __ __ y

 la__ __er

 ca__ __ot

 pi__ __a

 gra__ __ __

 bu__ __erfly

Say the name of each
picture. Spell the word
next to each picture.

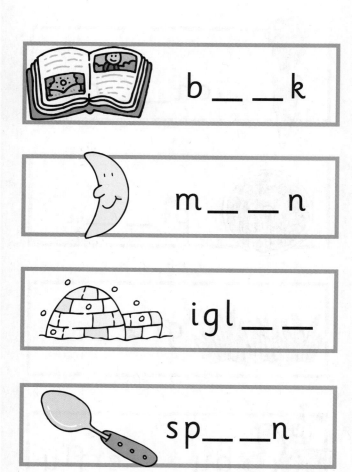

b _ _ k

m _ _ n

igl _ _

sp _ _ n

 ball__ __n

 kangar__ __

 d__ __r

 t__ __th

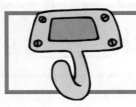 h__ __k

ow or ou?

Say what is in the picture.
Write <u>ow</u> or <u>ou</u> to make a word.

c _ _

cl_ _ n

m_ _ se

h_ _ se

_ _ l

fl_ _ers

rainb_ _

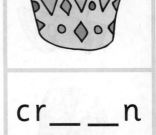

cr_ _n

wind_ _

 goat

 pear

 boat

 coat

 feather

Choose a word to fill each gap.

1. I felt sea sick on the

_____ .

2. I saw a _____ on
the farm.

3. I put on my _____ .

4. I can eat a _____ .

5. I found a _____ .

Middle sound: ai

Say what is in the picture.
Spell the word next to it.

___ a i ___

___ ___ a i ___

a i

___ ___   ___ ___ ___

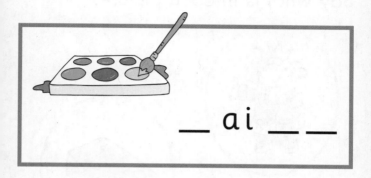

_ ai ___

_ ai _

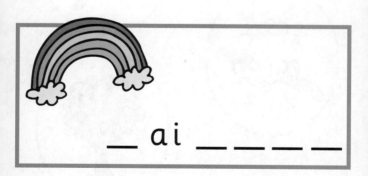

_ ai _____

ee or ea?

Say what is in each picture.

Spell the words you said.
Write each word on the
correct list. Check your spellings
in a dictionary.

ee	ea
cheese	

Fill in the missing letters. Choose <u>ai</u> as in snail or <u>ea</u> as in leaf. Write the whole word.

s _ _ t   tr _ _ n

_____   _____

b _ _ k

_____

t _ _ l

_____

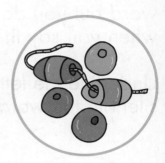

b _ _ ds

_____

r _ _ n

_____

Some words have silent letters. You see a silent letter in a word but you do not hear it when you say the word.

Underline the letters that are silent in the words below.

knife

guitar

knight

wheel

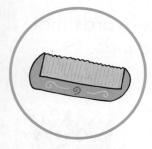

comb

thumb

wrist

badge

gnome

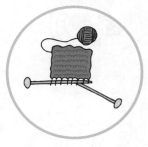

knitting

Rhyming words

Draw lines to join the words that end with the same sounds.

Choose words from this list to complete the rhyme.

out   sprout   spout   shout
rain   train   again

Incy Wincy Spider climbed up the water _____.

Down came the rain and washed the spider _____.

Out came the sunshine and dried up all the _____.

Now Incy Wincy Spider climbed up the spout _____!

Same sounds

Some words rhyme but have very different spelling patterns.

Write a word under each picture. Draw a line to join the words that rhyme.

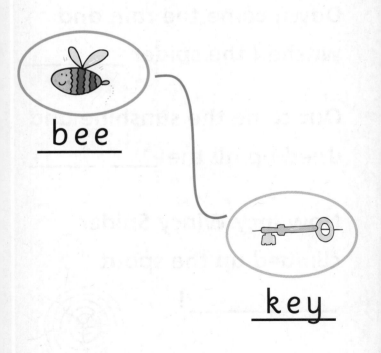

<u>b e e</u>

<u>k e y</u>

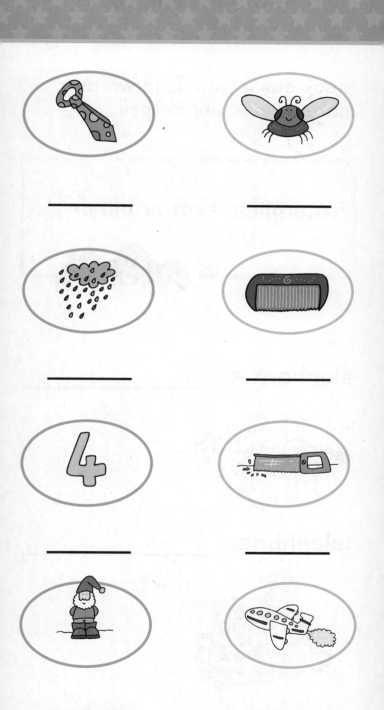

_____

_____

_____

_____

_____

_____

_____

_____

Break down these long words to make them easier to spell.

caterpillar = cat-er-pill-ar

elephant = _____

telephone = _____

magician = _____

policewoman = _____

banana = _____

butterfly = _____

Breaking down words

See if you can do this. The first one has been done for you.

Try it!

hammer

h–am–mer

cloud

_____

flower _____

church _____

crown _____

spider _____

Copy the words from the box into the right sentences.

laugh	because	here
once	water	would

I. I _____ **like a new bike.**

2. I am staying indoors _____ **it is raining.**

3. My sister likes to make me _____ .

4. I _____ went to a football match.

5. I wash with _____ .

6. _____ is my house.

Colours

LOOK at the word. COVER it up.
WRITE it on the line. CHECK if
you are right!

blue _____

green _____

red _____

orange _____

yellow _____

pink _____

 purple _____

 black _____

 white _____

 grey _____

 brown _____

Days of the week

Finish these sentences.

On _____ I go swimming.

On_____I play football.

On_____I feed the ducks.

Thursday

On _____
**I help Dad do
the shopping.**

Friday

On _____
**I go to see
my gran.**

Saturday

On _____
I go to a party.

Sunday

On_____
**I help Mum
wash her car.**

Compound words

A compound word is made up of two short ones. Write a word under each picture. Join two pictures to make a compound word.

star

fish

Now write your new words.

starfish
_____

_____

_____

_____

_____

Compound words

Write a word under each picture. Join two pictures to make a compound word.

_____

_____

_____

_____

_____

_____

_____

_____

Now write your new words.

_____

_____

_____

_____

Patterns in words

Read the word above each row.
Circle the pictures that end with
the same letters.

p<u>ick</u>

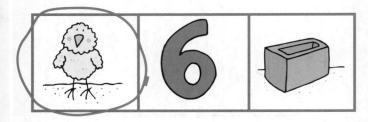

r<u>est</u>

l<u>ate</u>

thi<u>stle</u>

si<u>ght</u>

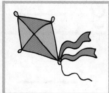 

ri<u>ng</u>

Hidden words

Find one little word hiding in each big word. Write the little words in the spaces.

I. balloon	___
2. supper	___
3. something	___
4. mother	___
5. horse	___
6. kitten	___
7. dinosaur	___
8. winter	___

Write sentences using four of the
words that you found.

1. _____

_____

2. _____

_____

3. _____

_____

4. _____

_____

Join each sentence to the right picture. Copy the word into the space by the picture.

1. A banana is a yellow fruit. You peel off its skin.

2. A brush is used for painting.

3. A butterfly is an insect with pretty wings.

4. A panda is a big black and white animal.

5. You wear a sock on your foot.

6. A frog lives by water. It can jump a long way.

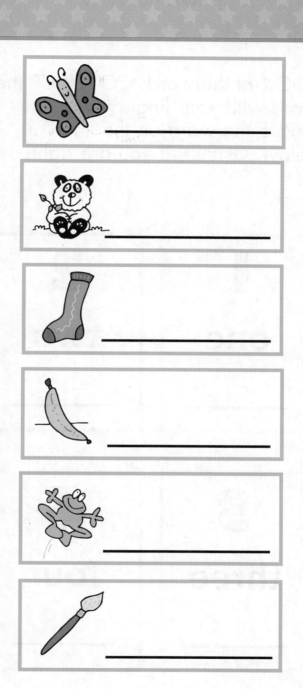

Numbers

LOOK at the word. COVER UP the word with your finger.
WRITE the word on the line below. CHECK if you are right!

1

one

_____

2

two

_____

3

three

_____

4

four

_____

5

five

_____

6

six

_____

7

seven

_____

8

eight

_____

9

nine

_____

10

ten

_____

More numbers

LOOK at the word. COVER UP the word with your finger. WRITE the word on the line below. CHECK if you are right!

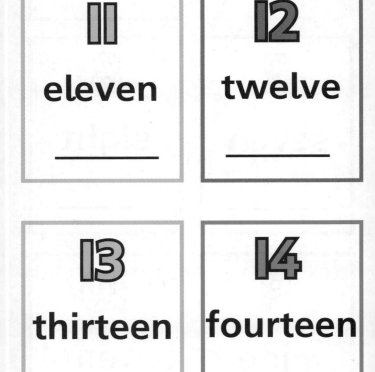

11 eleven

_____

12 twelve

_____

13 thirteen

_____

14 fourteen

_____

15
fifteen
_____

16
sixteen
_____

17
seventeen
_____

18
eighteen
_____

19
nineteen
_____

20
twenty
_____

Magic e

Add the letter <u>e</u> to a short word and magic happens.
The letter in the middle of the word changes its sound and the word changes its meaning.

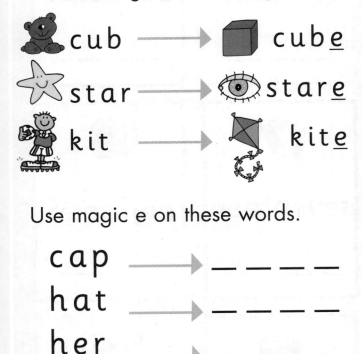

cub ⟶ cub<u>e</u>

star ⟶ star<u>e</u>

kit ⟶ kit<u>e</u>

Use magic e on these words.

cap ⟶ _ _ _ _

hat ⟶ _ _ _ _

her ⟶ _ _ _ _

bit ⟶ _ _ _ _

not ⟶ _ _ _ _

tub ⟶ _ _ _ _

The middles are missing from these words. Put the same missing letter in each pair of words, like this:

rid **and** rid<u>e</u>

Choose from:

a	e	i	o	u

1. c _ t   **and**   c _ t e
2. m _ t   **and**   m _ t e
3. p _ n   **and**   p _ n e
4. h _ p   **and**   h _ p e
5. c _ r   **and**   c _ r e
6. f _ n   **and**   f _ n e

Adding le

Add le to make a word. Then copy each word out. Can you find six of the words in the yellow box?

bicyc_ _   _____

tab_ _   _____

need_ _   _____

cand_ _   _____

beet_ _   _____

bott_ _ _____

jung_ _ _____

kett_ _ _____

a	t	a	b	l	e	c
k	n	q	e	i	f	k
e	n	e	e	d	l	e
b	o	t	t	l	e	t
o	s	d	l	m	g	t
h	j	p	e	r	w	l
b	i	c	y	c	l	e

Adding ing

Make six new words by adding <u>ing</u> to these letters. Then write each word in a sentence.

k _ _ _   sw_ _ _

sl _ _ _   w_ _ _

str_ _ _   r _ _ _

1. _____

_____

2. _____

_____

3. _____

_____

4. _____

_____

5. _____

_____

6. _____

_____

More than one

Copy these words into the right boxes.

mouse	book	house
fox	cow	tooth
foxes	houses	cows
books	mice	teeth

One	More than one
mouse	mice
tooth	teeth

Copy these words into the
right boxes.

lambs	child	boxes
lamb	glove	babies
children	gloves	box
cherry	baby	cherries

One	More than one
box	boxes
glove	gloves

Present and past

The present is something we are doing now. The past is something we have already done.

Present – I am painting a picture.

Past – I have painted a picture.

Add <u>ing</u> for the present and <u>ed</u> for the past.

Present	Past
wait _ _ _	wait _ _
jump _ _ _	jump _ _

Present	Past
sail _ _ _	sail _ _
walk _ _ _	walk _ _
talk _ _ _	talk _ _
crawl _ _ _	crawl _ _
climb _ _ _	climb _ _
wash _ _ _	wash _ _
brush _ _ _	brush _ _
laugh _ _ _	laugh _ _
cook _ _ _	cook _ _

Present and past

Here are some more words in the present and in the past, but these are much trickier. They don't follow the usual rules. You will have to learn them by heart.

Present	Past
swimming	swam
sleeping	slept
singing	sang
running	ran
crying	cried
drawing	drew
eating	ate
reading	read

COVER UP the word lists on the opposite page.
WRITE the missing words in the lists below.
CHECK if you are right!

Present	Past
swimming	_ _ _ _ _
sleeping	_ _ _ _ _ _
_ _ _ _ _ _ _ _	sang
running	_ _ _
_ _ _ _ _ _ _	cried
_ _ _ _ _ _ _ _	drew
eating	_ _ _
reading	_ _ _ _ _

113

Tricky words

Some words are tricky to spell because they don't follow normal spelling patterns. Here are some of them.

 anchor

 biscuit

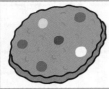 chef

 saucer

 penguin

 pyjamas

 whistle

Copy out any of these words
you find hard to spell. Cover
them up, then write them from
memory. Keep going until you
know the spelling.

_____

_____

_____

_____

Test your spelling

Say what is in each picture.
Spell the word next to it.

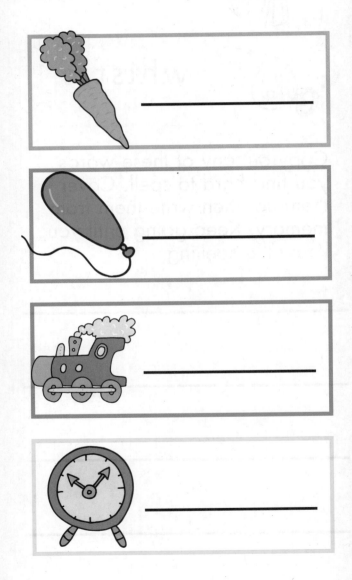

Now you can check your answers at the back of the book!

All these words are muddled up. Write them correctly. You can use a dictionary to help you.

	wrong ✗	right ✓
	lgri	_____
	bocm	_____
	lold	_____

	wrong ✗	right ✓
	ekti	_____
	rodo	_____
	rhia	_____
	rumd	_____
	ambl	_____
	cukd	_____

Right spellings

Choose the right word and put a tick in the box beside it.

1. Part of the foot.

| toe | |
| tow | |

2. A kind of fruit.

| bury | |
| berry | |

3. A very large sea animal.

| wail | |
| whale | |

4. To listen to a sound.

| here | |
| hear | |

5. Not old.

| new | |
| knew | |

6. Not strong.

| week | |
| weak | |

Now write the word.

1. _____

2. _____

3. _____

4. _____

5. _____

6. _____

Answers

Pages 8–9 Writing names

1. Sarah 2. Jack 3. Eva 4. Tom 5. Lily 6. Josh

Pages 10–11 First letter sounds

<u>e</u>gg <u>a</u>nt <u>c</u>ap <u>d</u>og <u>g</u>oat <u>h</u>en <u>b</u>ox <u>f</u>ish
1. ant 2. box 3. cap 4. dog 5. egg 6. fish 7. goat 8. hen

Pages 12–13 Letters i to r

The <u>k</u>ing and <u>q</u>ueen had lots of pets.

They had a <u>l</u>ion, and a <u>m</u>onkey and a <u>p</u>ig.

They had an <u>o</u>wl in a <u>n</u>est.

They had a <u>r</u>abbit with big ears.

They fed them all on <u>j</u>elly and <u>i</u>ce-cream.

ice-cream, jelly, king, lion, monkey, nest, owl, pig, queen, rabbit

Pages 14–15 First letter sounds

<u>t</u>ap <u>v</u>an <u>w</u>asp <u>y</u>ellow <u>z</u>ip
<u>u</u>mbrella <u>x</u>-ray <u>s</u>un
1. sun 2. tap 3. umbrella 4. van
5. wasp 6. x-ray 7. yellow 8. zip

Pages 16–17 Animal alphabet

camel   horse   fox   dragon

goat   ape   bear   elephant

1. ape 2. bear 3. camel 4. dragon
5. elephant 6. fox 7. goat 8. horse

Pages 18–19 Food alphabet

ice-cream   milk   jam   pizza   orange   lemon

1. ice-cream 2. jam 3. lemon 4. milk 5. orange 6. pizza

Pages 20–21 w words
1. <u>What</u> time is it?
2. <u>Where</u> are you going?
3. <u>Who</u> is your best friend?

4. <u>When</u> is your birthday?
5. <u>Why</u> are you sad?
6. <u>Was</u> it a good game?

Pages 22–23 Short vowel 'a'

c<u>a</u>t   b<u>a</u>t   r<u>a</u>t   h<u>a</u>t   1. bag 2. dad 3. map 4. fat

Pages 24–25 Short vowel 'e'

w<u>e</u>b   n<u>e</u>t   b<u>e</u>d   r<u>e</u>d   1. ten 2. fed 3. pen 4. wet

Pages 26–27 short vowel 'i'

p<u>i</u>g   s<u>i</u>x   w<u>i</u>g   p<u>i</u>n   1. dig 2. lick 3. big 4. did

Pages 28–29 Short vowel 'o'

d<u>o</u>g   f<u>o</u>x   m<u>o</u>p   l<u>o</u>g   1. got 2. on 3. top 4. hot

Pages 30–31 Short vowel 'u'

b<u>u</u>s   c<u>u</u>p   d<u>u</u>ck   s<u>u</u>n   1. run 2. hug 3. mum 4. mud

Pages 32–33 Second chance

d<u>o</u>g, c<u>u</u>p, p<u>i</u>g, b<u>a</u>t, b<u>e</u>d, w<u>i</u>g, c<u>a</u>t, f<u>o</u>x, w<u>e</u>b, d<u>u</u>ck, n<u>e</u>t, s<u>u</u>n, r<u>a</u>t, b<u>u</u>s

Pages 34–35 Three-letter words

deb = bed, ibb = bib, gge = egg, tca = cat, oyb = boy, acr = car, ebe = bee, ubs = bus, tab = bat

Pages 36–37 ch sound

<u>ch</u>air, <u>ch</u>ick, <u>ch</u>erry, <u>ch</u>ildren, <u>ch</u>ocolate, <u>ch</u>eese, <u>ch</u>ur<u>ch</u>

Pages 38–39 Look carefully

hutch: watch/switch/witch   sack: brick/sock/duck

Answers

Pages 40–41 Wordsearch for sh

s	h	a	r	k	n	b
h	m	f	o	d	e	r
e	d	i	s	h	s	u
e	h	s	r	u	l	s
p	s	h	e	d	o	h

shark   brush   shed   sheep

dish   fish

Pages 42–43 br sound

<u>br</u>ain, <u>br</u>anch, <u>br</u>oom, <u>br</u>idle, <u>br</u>ook, <u>br</u>ing, <u>br</u>im, <u>br</u>eeze, <u>br</u>onze, <u>br</u>ave

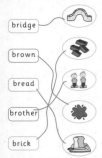

bridge

brown

bread

brother

brick

Pages 44–45 cr sound

<u>cr</u>y, <u>cr</u>ash, <u>cr</u>ew, <u>cr</u>isp, <u>cr</u>umb, <u>cr</u>unch, <u>cr</u>eak, <u>cr</u>eam, <u>cr</u>ate, <u>cr</u>ocodile

		c	r	a	b	
		r				
c	r	a	y	o	n	
r		c				
o		c	r	o	s	s
w		d				
n		i				
		l				
		e				

Pages 46–47 dr or tr

<u>dr</u>um, <u>dr</u>ink, <u>tr</u>actor, <u>dr</u>agon, <u>tr</u>iangle, <u>tr</u>uck
1. dragon 2. drum 3. drink 4. tractor

Pages 48–49 Sounds: st str sp sl sw

<u>st</u>ar, <u>sp</u>oon, <u>st</u>amp, <u>sw</u>ing, <u>str</u>awberry, <u>sl</u>ide

Pages 50–51 Wordsearch for bl cl fl

c	l	c	b	l	u	e
l	f	l	b	l	f	e
f	l	o	w	e	r	s
l	a	c	l	o	u	d
g	g	k	c	h	l	b
z	b	k	b	b	l	l
y	l	b	l	a	c	k

blue

cloud

flowers

clock

flag

black

Pages 52–53 th sound

<u>th</u>umb, <u>th</u>rone, <u>th</u>ree, <u>th</u>istle, ba<u>th</u>,
too<u>th</u>brush, ma<u>th</u>s

Pages 54–55 Double letters: ll

be<u>ll</u>, wa<u>ll</u>, ba<u>ll</u>, je<u>ll</u>y, umbre<u>ll</u>a, ro<u>ll</u>er skate, ye<u>ll</u>ow, ba<u>ll</u>oons,
caterpi<u>ll</u>ars

Pages 56–57 Double letters: dd rr tt ss zz

bo<u>tt</u>le, ke<u>tt</u>le, te<u>dd</u>y, che<u>rr</u>y, la<u>dd</u>er, ca<u>rr</u>ot, pi<u>zz</u>a, gra<u>ss</u>,
bu<u>tt</u>erfly

Pages 58–59 Double letters: oo

b<u>oo</u>k, m<u>oo</u>n, igl<u>oo</u>, sp<u>oo</u>n, ball<u>oo</u>n, kangar<u>oo</u>, d<u>oo</u>r, t<u>oo</u>th,
h<u>oo</u>k

Pages 60–61 ow or ou?

c<u>ow</u>, cl<u>ow</u>n, m<u>ou</u>se, h<u>ou</u>se, <u>ow</u>l, fl<u>ow</u>ers, rainb<u>ow</u>, cr<u>ow</u>n,
wind<u>ow</u>

Pages 62–63 Middle sound: oa and ea

1. I felt sea sick on the <u>boat</u>.
2. I saw a <u>goat</u> on the farm.
3. I put on my <u>coat</u>.
4. I can eat a <u>pear</u>.
5. I found a <u>feather</u>.

Pages 64–65 Middle sound: ai

<u>rain</u>, <u>train</u>, <u>trainer</u>, <u>paint</u>, <u>hair</u>, <u>rainbow</u>

Answers

Pages 66–67 ee or ea

ee	ea
cheese	ice-cream
queen	leaf
wheel	
tree	

Pages 68–69 Different middles ai ae

s<u>ea</u>t, tr<u>ai</u>n, b<u>ea</u>k, t<u>ai</u>l, b<u>ea</u>ds, r<u>ai</u>n

Pages 70–71 Silent letters

<u>k</u>nife/guitar/<u>k</u>night/w<u>h</u>eel/com<u>b</u>/thum<u>b</u>/<u>w</u>rist/ba<u>d</u>ge/<u>g</u>nome/<u>k</u>nitting

Pages 72–73 Rhyming words

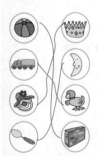

Incy Wincy Spider climbed up the water <u>spout.</u>

Down came the rain and washed the spider <u>out.</u>

Out came the sunshine and dried up all the <u>rain.</u>

Now Incy Wincy Spider climbed up the spout <u>again!</u>

Pages 74–75 Same sounds

tie/fly, rain/plane, four/saw, gnome/comb

Pages 76–77 Word syllables

Possible answers are: el-e-phant, tel-e-phone, mag-i-cian, pol-ice-woman, ba-na-na, but-ter-fly

Pages 78–79 Breaking down words

cl-oud, fl-ow-er, ch-ur-ch, cr-ow-n, sp-i-der

Pages 80–81 Everyday words

1. would 2. because 3. laugh 4. once 5. water 6. Here

Pages 84–85 Days of the week

On <u>Monday</u> I go swimming.
On <u>Tuesday</u> I play football.
On <u>Wednesday</u> I feed the ducks.
On <u>Thursday</u> I help Dad do the shopping.
On <u>Friday</u> I go to see my gran.
On <u>Saturday</u> I go to a party.
On <u>Sunday</u> I help Mum wash her car.

Pages 86–87 Compound words

star+fish = starfish, butter+fly = butterfly,
cow+boy = cowboy, horse+shoe = horseshoe
rain+bow = rainbow

Pages 88–89 Compound words

pig+tail = pigtail, jelly+fish = jellyfish,
hair+brush = hairbrush, drum+stick = drumstick

Pages 90–91 Patterns in words

ick
est
ate
tle
ight
ing

Pages 92–93 Hidden words

You can find more than one little word in some big words.
1. ball, all, on 2. up 3. some, thing, met, in, thin, so, me
4. the, her, moth, he 5. or 6. ten, kit, it 7. in, din, no 8. win, in

Pages 94–95 Definitions

butterfly   panda   sock   banana   frog   brush

Pages 100–101 Magic e

cap–cape, hat–hate, her–here, bit–bite, not–note, tub–tube

1. cut and cute 2. mat and mate 3. pin and pine
4. hop and hope 5. car and care 6. fin and fine

Answers

Pages 102–103 Adding le

bicyc<u>le</u>, tab<u>le</u>, need<u>le</u>, cand<u>le</u>, beet<u>le</u>, bott<u>le</u>, jung<u>le</u>, kett<u>le</u>

Pages 104–105 Adding ing

k<u>ing</u>, sw<u>ing</u>, sl<u>ing</u>, w<u>ing</u>, str<u>ing</u>, r<u>ing</u>

Pages 106–107 More than one

One: mouse/book/house/fox/cow/tooth
More than one: mice/books/houses/foxes/cows/teeth

Pages 108–109 More than one

One: box/glove/lamb/child/baby/cherry
More than one: boxes/gloves/lambs/children/babies/cherries

Pages 110–111 Present and past

<u>Present</u>	<u>Past</u>
wait<u>ing</u>	wait<u>ed</u>
jump<u>ing</u>	jump<u>ed</u>
sail<u>ing</u>	sail<u>ed</u>
walk<u>ing</u>	walk<u>ed</u>
talk<u>ing</u>	talk<u>ed</u>
crawl<u>ing</u>	crawl<u>ed</u>
climb<u>ing</u>	climb<u>ed</u>
wash<u>ing</u>	wash<u>ed</u>
brush<u>ing</u>	brush<u>ed</u>
laugh<u>ing</u>	laugh<u>ed</u>
cook<u>ing</u>	cook<u>ed</u>

Pages 116–117 Test your spelling

carrot, balloon, train, clock, flag, bridge, bottle, starfish

Pages 118–119 Right spellings

lgri = girl, bocm = comb, lold = doll, ekti = kite, rodo = door,
rhia = hair, rumd = drum, ambl = lamb, cukd = duck

Pages 120–121 Right spellings

1. toe 2. berry 3. whale 4. hear 5. new 6. weak